GW00320250

Juicing

Freshly made juices for a healthy and energised life

Juicing

Freshly made juices for a healthy and energised life

Tracy Rutherford

APPLE

Contents

Introduction 7

Glossary 8

Equipment 10
Juicer • Blender • Grinder
• Juice extractors • Citrus juicers

Ingredients and Supplements 13
Dairy and non-dairy products • Liquids

Herbal Preparations and Nutritional Supplements 16

Creating Flavor 18
Sweeteners • Nuts and seeds • Spices

RECIPES

Cleansing 25

Energy 37

Workout 51

Stress and Relaxation 63

Tonics and Remedies 73

Immunity and Prevention 87

Juice Plans 101

Three-day cleansing juice plan
- Day one
- Day two
- Day three
- Pre-exam juice plan
- Tips for studying
- Sporting-event juice plan
- The big event juice plan

Glossary 107

Index 108

Guide to Weights and Measures 111

Recipes

Cleansing 25
Super "Orange" juice 26 • Prune and apple drink 26 • Grape and dandelion juice 26
• Orange, ginger and herb drink 29 • Cranberry and barley drink 29 • Spinach and red
pepper juice 29 • Fennel, pear and mint juice 30 • Mango and lychee juice 30
• Carrot, celery and arugula juice 30 • Cantaloupe, blueberry and mint juice 32
• Carrot, apple and cucumber juice 32 • Watercress and orange juice 32
• Beet, spinach and pear juice 35 • Radish, parsley and carrot juice 35
• Peach, plum and raspberry juice 35

Energy 37
Banana and mango frappé 39 • Strawberry and watermelon booster 39 • Cantaloupe
and papaya juice 39 • Breakfast in a glass 40 • Fig, plum and soy shake 40
• Orange, pineapple and mango juice 40 • Peach, apricot and tahini blend 43
• Carob and strawberry milk shake 43 • Nectarine, pineapple and ginseng drink 43
• Pineapple and coconut drink 44 • Spinach, carrot and orange juice 44 • Pear and
date drink 44 • Kiwi and cantaloupe juice with spirulina 47 • Beet and carrot juice
with rosemary 47 • Peach and raisin smoothie 47 • Prune, honey and oat milk
drink 48 • Plum, black currant and grape juice 48 • Apple and citrus juice 48

Workout 51
Pear, peach and apricot juice 53 • Orange and broccoli booster 53 • Banana and fig
super smoothie 53 • Orange, cucumber and parsley juice 54 • Cantaloupe and
pineapple recovery juice 54 • Plum and berry blend 54 • Pineapple and papaya
cooler 57 • Banana, carob and peanut butter smoothie 57 • Pear and almond shake 57
• Melon, grape and lychee juice 58 • Grapefruit, papaya and mango juice 58
• Carrot, orange and ginger juice 58 • Apricot and Brazil blend 61 • Peach and ginger
thick shake 61 • Tomato and cabbage revitalizer 61

Stress and Relaxation 63

Mulled rose hip tea 65 • Watermelon cooler 65 • Warm spiced milk 65 • Peach and raspberry cocktail 66 • Warm apple and chamomile drink 66 • Strawberry soother 66 • Pineapple, ginger and lemon juice 69 • Tomato and basil aperitif 69 • Warming apricot smoothie 69 • Tropical colada 70 • Melon-berry crush 70 • Soothing citrus iced tea 70

Tonics and Remedies 73

Cranberry, pear and lime juice 75 • Fennel, parsley and apricot juice 75 • Apricot and bilberry juice 75 • Kiwi cold fighter 77 • Celery and apple juice 77 • Grapefruit, lemon and ginger juice 78 • Apple, prune and aloe juice 78 • Melon mouth healer 78 • Tomato tonic 80 • Pineapple and grape juice 80 • Fennel and mint drink 80 • Orange and herb brew 83 • Ginger and coriander seed tea 83 • Guava and rice milk blend 84 • Strawberry and rose hip skin tonic 84

Immunity and Prevention 87

Mango mix 89 • Orange and ginger juice 89 • Tomato and watercress juice 89 • Carrot and orange juice 90 • Wheatgrass booster 90 • Banana bone builder 90 • Spinach and orange juice 93 • Red pepper, carrot and celery juice 93 • Apple and alfalfa juice 93 • Beet and broccoli juice 94 • Super-C juice 94 • Strawberry shake 94 • Melon and mint juice 97 • Papaya and pineapple juice 97 • Sesame-bok choy blend 97 • Berry and orange juice 98 • Citrus immunity booster 98 • Tofu thick shake 98

Introduction

J*uicing* is a collection of juices, smoothies, shakes, and teas designed to provide maximum nutrition with a minimum of fuss. It is sometimes difficult to incorporate the recommended daily servings of fruit and vegetables into our diet, but juicing and blending offer convenient and delicious ways of doing so. These are also great ways to get children to consume more fruit, though juices should be diluted with purified water for young children, and the eating of whole fruits and vegetables encouraged as much as possible. If you have any kind of blood sugar disorder, it is also recommended that you dilute juices, as they do contain a concentrated supply of fruit sugars.

When making juices, the final product will only be as good as the ingredients used, so always choose fruits and vegetables that are ripe, but not overly so, and that look bright and fresh. Use produce in season, as it will be cheaper, fresher, and in optimum condition. If you can, buy organic produce, as many fruits and vegetables are juiced with their skin still on, and the skin may harbor residual chemicals. Also, if you are taking the time to create fresh juices at home, it makes sense to use the healthiest ingredients possible.

Unpeeled fruits and vegetables must always be cleaned thoroughly before use. Use a small, firm-bristled brush kept specifically for this purpose. If the produce is not organic, use a mild biodegradable detergent to remove all traces of chemicals, and rinse thoroughly. The recipes indicate how each fruit or vegetable is to be prepared for juicing, usually they just need to be chopped into pieces that will fit into the feed tube. You may want to chill produce before juicing for some recipes, but this is a matter of taste.

Juicers vary considerably in power and efficiency. If you have an older or slightly less-efficient juicer, you may find you need to add small pieces like berries and grapes to the feed tube while the motor is turned off, then turn it on and plunge them all together. Fresh herbs and other leaves should be placed between fleshier pieces of fruit or vegetable where possible, to help extract as much juice as possible. We have given approximate yields for each drink, though this will vary depending on your equipment and produce.

The combinations of ingredients given for the drinks may be varied to suit your taste and their availability. Some of the recipes list optional ingredients. These are mostly supplements with specific applications that may be useful to athletes or to treat ailments. Feel free to use them or not, or to seek further information about them from a naturopath or your natural food store.

The drinks in this book provide concentrated nutrition, and some can be used to assist in the treatment of specific conditions, but you should always consult a health-care professional for advice. Most of the drinks are delicious, as you would expect from the combinations of fresh, juicy fruits and vegetables, while some are slightly more medicinal. Each chapter is devoted to a specific use, though fruits, vegetables, and other ingredients that may help one condition usually are good for others as well.

Equipment

The pieces of equipment required to make the drinks in this book are a blender, a juicer, a grinder, and a citrus juicer. You probably already have some of these, but if you are shopping for new appliances consider the following factors and choose the best quality you can afford.

Juicer

ꕤ Check for ease of cleaning and assembling. Does the juicer have a lot of components to deal with, or does it have grooves or other hard-to-clean crevices? Look for a simple, streamlined machine.

ꕤ What is the size and position of pulp container? If making large quantities of juice, will you have to stop and take the machine apart often to clear out pulp, and if so, is it easy to do? Some juicers have external pulp collection areas, which means you don't have to disassemble anything to empty them.

ꕤ How powerful is the motor? Will it extract the maximum amount of juice?

ꕤ Check for safety and ease of use. Does the lid have a safety lock? Are the controls easy to use?

Similar considerations apply to blenders, electric citrus juicers, and grinders. If you are still unsure, look at the brand reputation and the warranty conditions in case something does go wrong. It is also a good idea to check consumer guides for price and workability comparisons.

Another important point to consider is where you will keep your machine. Do you have room on your countertop to leave it set up all the time? Will it fit in an easy-to-reach cupboard? Accessibility is vital, as many juicers are bought with the best intentions, only to languish, forgotten, in dark cupboards.

Blender

Grinder

Juice extractor: Centrifugal

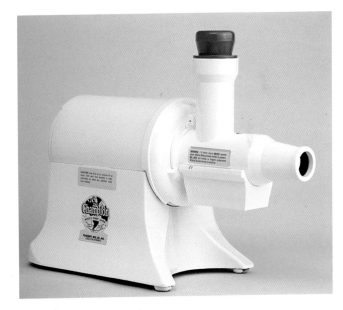

Juice extractor: Masticating

Citrus juicer: Reamer

Citrus juicer: Manual juicer

Citrus juicer: Electric juicer

Citrus juicer: Press/lever juicer

Blender

A blender is used to liquidize soft fruits for drinks, as well as to make milk-based shakes and smoothies. Be sure yours will handle ice cubes, which can overwork less powerful motors. If not, wrap ice cubes in a clean tea towel and crush them with a rolling pin or mallet before blending.

Grinder

A grinder is used to grind nuts and seeds to a meal or fine powder. This not only changes them into a form suitable for drinks, but also in some cases makes them more digestible. An electric coffee grinder is probably the most efficient grinder, but you will need to keep it specifically for nuts and seeds, so as not to transfer a coffee flavor.

Juice Extractors

There are different types of extractors, but the two types normally used in domestic situations are either a centrifugal extractor or a masticating extractor, with the former being the most common.

A centrifugal machine extracts juice by finely grating food, then using centrifugal force (spinning around very fast) to separate the juice from the pulp. This tends to aerate the juice, which should be consumed straight away, as it will deteriorate rapidly.

A masticating machine also finely grates the food, but then has a "chewing" action that makes the particles even smaller. This pulp is pressed to extract the juice, so it doesn't incorporate air. This means that the juice can be stored for up to one day in the refrigerator.

Citrus Juicers

Citrus fruits can be peeled and juiced in an extractor, but if you are only juicing one or two pieces of a citrus fruit, you may want to use a citrus juicer. There are four kinds:

Reamer: A small handheld tool with a handle at one end and a corrugated, rounded cone at the other. The reamer is inserted into the cut fruit and twisted to extract juice.

Manual juicer: A small, freestanding juicer with a "cone" standing upright, with either a juice collection gutter around it or holes draining into a jug. The cut fruit is twisted by hand to extract the juice.

Electric juicer: A comparatively large piece of equipment, the cut fruit is held in place by hand, while a motor spins the "cone." The juice drains through a spout into a collection pitcher.

Press/lever juicer: This type of manual juicer has styles that can vary slightly, but they work on the principle of the pressure—the cut citrus half is placed on the cone, then you pull a lever to exert pressure, releasing the juice. These are very stylish pieces, usually made from stainless steel with some chrome parts.

Ingredients and Supplements

Dairy and Non-dairy Products

Acidophilus yogurt is made with the bacteria culture *Lactobacillus acidophilus*. Eating this yogurt helps restore the intestinal bacteria lost through illness or the use of antibiotics.

Coconut milk is made by squeezing liquid from grated coconut flesh. It is available in cans in most supermarkets.

Cows' milk is the most widely used kind of milk, and thus one of the most common sources of calcium. Some people, however, have an intolerance to lactose, the sugar present in milk, and must use an alternative.

Oat milk is an alternative to cows' milk, made from whole-grain oats, a little oil, and water. Found in cartons in natural food stores and some supermarkets.

Rice milk, another milk alternative, is made from whole-grain brown rice and usually contains some kind of oil, a little salt, and water. Available in cartons from natural food stores and some supermarkets.

Soy milk is made from soybeans and may contain other ingredients such as malt, oil, and rice syrup. Choose calcium-fortified brands, and look for organic soy milk whenever possible to avoid a genetically modified product, as well as undesirable chemicals.

Soy yogurt is made from soy milk. Look for brands that contain acidophilus culture.

Silken tofu is another soy product, made by adding a setting agent to soy milk. Tofu can either be firm or soft, the latter is best for drinks and desserts, as it has a very soft texture.

Liquids

Barley water is made by boiling pearl barley in water and draining off the resulting liquid, which is slightly thick. It is very nutritious.

Coconut water is the clear liquid found in the center of a coconut. It is obtained by piercing the coconut shell with a sharp implement, such as a pick, tapped with a hammer.

Rose water is a flavoring used in Middle Eastern and Indian cooking. It is also said to have cooling, nourishing properties. Available from natural foods stores or specialty markets.

Acidophilus yogurt

Coconut milk

Cows' milk

Oat milk

Rice milk

Soy milk

Soy yogurt

Silken tofu

Barley water

Coconut water

Rose water

Herbal Preparations and Nutritional Supplements

Aloe vera juice is squeezed from the succulent leaves of the aloe vera plant. It is claimed to have many healing properties, and is available in bottles in the refrigerator at natural foods stores.

Blackstrap molasses is a by-product of sugar refining, and is the lowest grade of molasses, with dark color and slightly bitter flavor. It is rich in calcium and iron, among other nutrients. It is available from natural foods stores.

Brewer's yeast is a good natural source of B vitamins, protein, and chromium. It comes in a powder form, from natural foods stores. Do not confuse it with other types of yeast.

Chlorophyll liquid is a concentrated form of the substance that gives the green color to plants. It has healing properties and is often used to treat bad breath and body odor. Available from natural foods stores.

Echinacea drops are the liquid form of the immune-boosting herb echinacea. It is thought to be particularly useful at the onset of a cold or other respiratory ailments. Available from natural foods stores or herbal-medicine practitioners.

Ginkgo drops are the liquid form of the herb ginkgo biloba. It is said to stimulate circulation, relieve tinnitus, and aid memory. Available from natural foods stores.

Glucosamine is a substance that the body needs to build and repair cartilage and to maintain healthy joints. As a supplement, it may be useful to athletes or osteoarthritis sufferers. It comes in powder form from natural foods stores.

Guarana powder is made from ground seed of Paullinia cupana, a Brazilian rain-forest tree. It contains some caffeine and therefore has an "energy boost" effect similar to coffee. Available from natural foods stores and some supermarkets.

L-carnitine is an amino acid that helps the body to metabolize fat and utilize it as fuel. It comes in powder form from natural foods stores.

Aloe vera juice

Blackstrap molasses

Brewer's yeast

Chlorophyll liquid

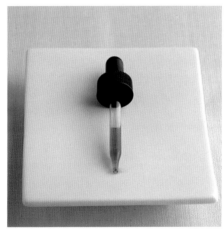

Echinacea drops

Ginkgo drops

Glucosamine

Guarana powder

L-carnitine

Lecithin is a substance that assists in the breakdown of fats and cholesterol. It may help to combat fat-related conditions such as arterial disease and gallstones. Available in granule form from natural foods stores.

Slippery elm powder is a finely ground bark. It is used mainly to soothe inflamed mucous membranes anywhere in the digestive system. Available from natural foods stores.

Protein whey powder is a dairy by-product. It is a source of amino acids, which are needed for muscle tissue maintenance. You can buy it as an expensive sports drink powder, which includes other ingredients (such as sugar and flavorings), or as a less expensive, unadorned supplement from health foods stores.

Spirulina powder is made from various types of algae, and has a concentration of many nutrients. It is believed to be a good source of protein, especially for vegetarians, as it contains all the essential amino acids. Available from natural foods stores.

Psyllium husks are a gentle soluble fiber that passes through the body, helping to remove waste. Available from natural foods stores and some supermarkets.

Wheat germ is part of the wheat grain, discarded in the processing of white flour. It is very nutritious, rich in vitamin E and B vitamins. Available from natural foods stores and supermarkets.

Wheatgrass is a grass grown from wheat grain and harvested at a particular stage to yield the optimum concentration of nutrients. It is reputed to be an excellent source of vitamins (particularly B, C and E) and minerals (calcium, magnesium, potassium, and iron), as well as enzymes, amino acids, and chlorophyll. It must be made into juice to be properly digested.

Wheatgrass juice is the liquified form of wheatgrass. Regular domestic centrifugal juicers are not capable of producing wheatgrass juice, so either seek out a model which is, or purchase from the refrigerator section at health foods stores. It is highly perishable, and must be used within 36 hours of production.

Lecithin

Slippery elm powder

Protein whey powder

Spirulina powder

Psyllium husks

Wheat germ

Wheatgrass

Wheatgrass juice

Creating Flavor

Sweeteners

Palm sugar, used in Southeast Asian cooking, is made from the sap of coconut and palmyrah palms. The color varies from dark brown to light golden, and it has a crumbly texture. It is available in block form from specialty foods markets and natural foods stores.

Honey is widely available but varies in quality and flavor. Use raw honey (honey that has not been heated) from a natural foods store if possible.

Carob powder, ground from roasted carob pods, is similar in appearance, flavor, and texture to cocoa powder. Though not strictly a sweetener, it is often used as a chocolate substitute. It has many vitamins and minerals, and no caffeine.

Nuts and Seeds

Almond meal is simply almonds ground to a fine powder. You can buy it or make it yourself using a grinder.

Brazil nuts, sometimes known as para nuts, are a good source of magnesium. These relatively large, elongated, three-sided nuts originated in Brazil.

Flaxseed (linseed) meal is finely ground flaxseed. It is best to grind your own, as the oils tend to deteriorate quickly once ground.

Flaxseed oil is available in bottles from refrigerators in natural foods stores. It is highly perishable, so keep refrigerated and use before the marked expiry date.

Peanut butter is a paste made from ground peanuts. Choose natural peanut butter from natural foods stores, rather than varieties with added salt and sugar.

Sunflower seed meal must be made by grinding sunflower seeds, as it is not available already ground. The seeds are a good source of thiamine, vitamin E, and silicon.

Tahini is a paste made from sesame seeds. Commonly used in Middle Eastern dishes such as hummus, it is rich in minerals, particularly calcium, phosphorus, and magnesium.

SWEETENERS
Top: Palm sugar
Center: Honey
Bottom: Carob powder

NUTS AND SEEDS
Top: Flaxseed oil
Second row (left to right): Tahini, Peanut butter
Third row (left to right): Flaxseed meal, Brazil nuts
Bottom row (left to right): Sunflower seed meal, Almond meal

Spices

Asafoetida is a ground spice derived from a plant grown in India and the Middle East. In herbal medicine it is used to ease coughs and other respiratory problems, and to reduce gas. Also known as hing.

Black pepper is ground from dried black peppercorns. It is best to buy whole peppercorns and grind them yourself. Pepper aids digestion and circulation.

Cardamom, commonly used in Indian cooking, is available as whole pods, seeds, or ground. Cardamom is good for digestion, coughs, and colds.

Cinnamon can be bought ground or in stick form, as a piece of rolled bark. Used in both sweet and savory dishes, cinnamon is good for circulation and digestion.

Coriander seeds come from the cilantro, or fresh coriander, plant, and are used whole or ground. Found in many countries, coriander is an important component of various spice blends. It stimulates the digestive system and helps with urinary tract infections.

Cayenne pepper is ground from the dried cayenne chili. Used to add heat and spice in cooking, it also enhances circulation, is good for digestion, and acts as a decongestant.

Fenugreek seeds come from a plant that is a member of the pea family. Usually ground and added to curry blends, fenugreek has anti-inflammatory properties and is an expectorant.

Ginger is used fresh or dried and ground. It is good for digestion, circulation, and nausea, and is used in many sweet and savory dishes.

Saffron threads are the dried stigmas from a kind of crocus. It is hand-harvested and therefore quite expensive. Used in cooking for its flavor and to add a golden color to foods; in herbal medicine it is used to treat depression.

Vanilla extract is made from the vanilla bean, a highly fragrant pod containing tiny black seeds. It is used to flavor many sweet dishes and baked goods.

Nutmeg is a ground spice commonly used in sweet milky or egg-based desserts. Medicinally, it is used to help induce sleep.

SPICES
Top: Vanilla extract
Second row (left to right): Ground fenugreek, Ground coriander, Ground cardamom, Cinnamon sticks
Third row (left to right): Cayenne pepper, Ground ginger, Ground cinnamon, Ground black pepper
Bottom row (left to right): Coriander seeds, Ground nutmeg, Asafoetida, Saffron threads

GW00320203

TUSCANY
AND THE SURROUNDING REGIONS

TUSCAN RECIPES FOR
THE ADVENTUROUS COOK

TUSCANY

AND THE SURROUNDING REGIONS

TUSCAN RECIPES FOR
THE ADVENTUROUS COOK

Quantum
Books

A QUANTUM BOOK

Published by
Quantum Books Ltd
6 Blundell Street
London N7 9BH

Copyright ©1998 Quantum Books Ltd

All rights reserved.
This book is protected by copyright. No part of it may be
reproduced, stored in a retrieval system, or transmitted in
any form or by any means, without the prior permission in
writing of the Publisher, nor be otherwise circulated in any
form of binding or cover other than that in which it is
published and without a similar condition including this
condition being imposed on the subsequent publisher.

1-86160-201-4

Project Manager: Rebecca Kingsley
Designer: Bruce Low
Editor: Sarah Harris

The material in this publication previously appeared in
Italian Regional Cooking,
The Complete Italian Cookbook

QUMTSCN
Set in Fritz Quadrata
Reproduced in Singapore by Eray Scan
Printed in Singapore by Star Standard Industries (Pte) Ltd

Contents
....

INTRODUCTION

6

SOUPS AND STARTERS

10

FISH, CHICKEN AND GAME

16

MEAT DISHES

32

PASTA AND PRIMI PIATTI

48

INTRODUCTION

Tuscany and the surrounding regions in Italy are home to some of the most distinctive and delicious recipes in the world. The regional variations in the cuisine of this part of Italy stem largely from the fierce sense of local pride that the inhabitants hold for their traditional dishes. This pride has developed over centuries during which each region remained in relative isolation from its neighbours,

both politically and geographically. Indeed, it was only during the latter part of the nineteenth century that the regions were united. Today the diversity of Italian cookery is recognised and enjoyed throughout the world.

One of the main reasons that each region holds its own local dishes so dearly is that a great emphasis is placed on the use of fresh ingredients. With this in mind it is understandable that Italians make the best use of locally grown or raised produce, rather than journeying any distance to obtain ingredients. There is little doubt that fresh foods impart the best flavours, whether this is in the form of home-grown fruits and vegetables, or just-caught fish from the sea.

This respect for food, together with the emphasis placed on the quality of the ingredients is highlighted by one of the main characteristics of Italian cooking.

Unlike French food, for example, which often includes sophisticated sauces, Italian cooking is intended to bring out the natural flavours of the ingredients. It is this that gives the regions of Italy their

reputation for healthy, hearty meals. Home cooking at its best, Italian cuisine offers a varied range of recipes, many of which can be easily mastered by even the most inexperienced chef.

Tuscany and the surrounding regions have a deserved reputation for providing some of the tastiest dishes in Italian cuisine. Wholesome and delicious, as well as filling,

it is easy to understand why the inhabitants of these regions take such delight in their food. Although each region shares the preference for simplicity over sophistication, there are subtle differences between the regions, and each is known for particular specialities.

At the very heart of Italy, Tuscany is famed for its traditional cuisine. In the past, critics have been disdainful of the simplicity of Tuscan dishes, but today rustic cooking is no longer the poor relation in the culinary world. As people have become more health-conscious, the very lack of heavy, complex sauces makes traditional Tuscan fare both healthy and delicious. Beans feature heavily in the cooking of

this region, served in soups and risottos or with tuna as an appetiser. Game is also a staple ingredient, taking advantage of the rich hunting available in the Tuscan hills. In most cases this is simply roasted and lightly seasoned. Spinach is also widely used, leading to the use outside Italy of the culinary term 'alla fiorentina', meaning, with spinach. Any of the Tuscan recipes can be perfectly complemented with the famous wine from this region - Chianti.

The region of Lazio is known for its pasta dishes, featuring a variety of sauces such as alla carrettiera - tuna and mushroom and alla carbonara - bacon, eggs and cream. Pasta ranges from the sheet-based types such as canneloni, favoured in the north of the region, to the tubular pasta more common in the south. Another well-known and popular dish from the Lazio region is Saltimbocca, a dish of ham-topped veal.

Bologna, in the Emilia-Romagna region to the north-east of Tuscany, is also noted for its fresh pasta, and, of course, its famous spaghetti sauce! This region is one of the richest in terms of the sheer abundance of foods available, due largely to its lush climate and fertile soil. Emilia-Romagna is also home to the mortadella, one of Italy's finest sausages, and parmesan cheese.

The Liguria region, north of Tuscany shares many of its neighbours' priorities in regard to food preparation and cooking. Fish is a strong feature of many dishes, and freshness is of paramount importance. Such is the desire for the freshest possible foods throughout Italy, that fish dishes are served less frequently the further inland you go. This again emphasises the preference within each region for using mainly local ingredients. When there is an abundance of delicious food available close to hand, why bring in ingredients from elsewhere?

The recipes in this book have been selected to bring together the very best dishes from Tuscany and the surrounding regions. To enjoy the full flavour of each dish, it is important that you adopt the Italian approach to cooking, which in simple terms means the ingredients are everything! Choose the freshest cuts of meat and fish, and use fresh herbs where possible, although dried ones will certainly not detract from the taste. If you are lucky enough to be able to grow your own vegetables, this will add an extra touch to that authentic home-cooked flavour. You should also remember that these recipes have been handed down through the generations, and have been adapted

and goodness of the ingredients, these recipes will delight the adventurous and the health-conscious alike.

according each cook's preferences and choice. With this in mind, do not be afraid to experiment, by adding or substituting ingredients as you progress. You can be sure that by bringing out the natural taste

CHAPTER ONE

SOUPS AND STARTERS

JELLIED TOMATO MOUSSE

■

COOKED HAM IN GELATIN

■

BEAN AND VEGETABLE SOUP

■

CRAZY-CUT PASTA
ROMAGNOLA STYLE

Jellied Tomato Mousse
Mousse di Pomodoro in Gelatina

SERVES 4

Ingredients

450 g (1 lb) tomatoes, peeled, seeded, chopped

Salt

75 ml (2¼ floz) thick béchamel sauce

1 envelope unflavoured gelatin

75 ml (2¼ floz) dry sherry

525 ml (17½ floz) cups beef stock

½ pt whipping cream, whipped

Purée tomatoes in a blender or press through a strainer, season with salt and cook gently for 5 minutes. Put to drain in a cloth tied up at 4 corners over a bowl for 2½ hours. Mix drained tomatoes thoroughly with béchamel sauce; press through a strainer or process in a blender. Refrigerate for 20 minutes. Meanwhile, soften gelatin in sherry. Heat stock in a small pan; add softened gelatin and stir over low heat until completely dissolved. Chill until syrupy and slightly thickened. Pour half the gelatin mixture into a glass bowl and swirl to cover sides. Chill until set (do not refrigerate remaining gelatin mixture). Mix tomato mixture with a wooden spoon to give a soft, smooth consistency. Fold in whipped cream. Spoon into gelatin-coated bowl. If necessary, stir remaining gelatin mixture over low heat until liquefied; then pour over tomato mixture. Chill until set. Unmould onto a serving dish and serve.

COOKED HAM IN GELATIN
Prosciutto Cotto in Gelatina

SERVES 4

INGREDIENTS

8 slices cooked ham

1 envelope unflavoured gelatin

75 ml (2½ floz) dry sherry

525 ml (17½ floz) cups beef stock

Cut ham slices in half and roll them up. Soften gelatin in sherry. Heat stock in a small pan; add softened gelatin and stir over low heat until completely dissolved. Pour a little gelatin into bottom of a dish and refrigerate until set. Arrange ham rolls on gelatin; drizzle remaining gelatin over ham and chill for 2 hours. The ham rolls may also be stuffed with pâté or Russians salad.

BEAN AND VEGETABLE SOUP
Zuppa di Fagiolialla Marchigiana
SERVES 4

INGREDIENTS

30 g (1½ oz) chopped bacon
65 g (2½ oz) dried white beans, soaked
Salt
½ onion
½ stalk celery
½ bunch parsley
Vegetable oil
1 tbsp tomato purée
40 g (1½ oz) chopped green cabbage
40 g (1½ oz) peeled, chopped potato
25 g (1 oz) cauliflowerets
1 bunch beetroots, cooked, peeled, diced
Pepper
65 g (2½ oz) shelled fresh peas
4 slices toast

Blanch bacon, drain and put in a pan with beans. Pour in 2100 ml (3½ pt) water, season with salt, and cook until beans are done. Drain beans and reserve cooking liquid. Meanwhile, chop together onion, celery and parsley and fry in a large pan in a little oil until soft. Add tomato purée diluted with a little water. Pour in bean cooking liquid and stir in cabbage, potato, cauliflower and beetroots. Season with salt and pepper. Simmer soup for 30 minutes, adding more water if necessary.

Meanwhile, purée half the beans and cook peas separately. Add all beans and peas to soup and heat through. Put toast in a soup tureen and pour in the soup. Let it stand for a few minutes before serving.

CRAZY-CUT PASTA ROMAGNOLA STYLE

Malfattini alla Romagnola

SERVES 4

INGREDIENTS

65 g (2½ oz) plain flour

3 eggs, beaten

Salt

Pinch of ground nutmeg

900 ml (1½ pt) chicken or beef stock

Heap flour on work surface, make a well in the middle and add eggs and a pinch of salt and nutmeg. Form into a dough and knead mixture until it is smooth. Form dough into a rectangular loaf shape and leave to dry out a little. Cut it into thick slices and let dry a little longer. Chop coarsely and dry out completely. Pour stock into a pan and bring to the boil. Add pasta and cook for 2–3 minutes, then serve in soup bowls.

Chapter Two

Fish, Chicken and Game

Salmon Trout with Aïoli

■

Chicken Stuffed with Artichokes

■

Fried Stuffed Sardines

■

Red Mullet with Ham

■

Quail in Brandy with Peas

■

Sardines with Pepper and Tomato Sauce

■

Red Mullet Livorno Style

INGREDIENTS

1 900 g (2 lb) salmon trout (or use a large trout)

2 small carrots, chopped

1 stalk celery, chopped

2 small onions, chopped

1 tbsp chopped parsley

3 medium potatoes, peeled, sliced

4 cloves garlic

2 slices white bread, crusts trimmed, softened in vinegar

Salt and pepper

300 ml (½ pt) vegetable oil

Lemon wedges

12 g (½ oz) butter, melted

SALMON TROUT WITH AÏOLI
Trota Salmonata con Agliata alla Ligure
SERVES 4

Clean and wash trout, put in a fish kettle or a pan that it will fit and cover with a court bouillon made from 1800 ml (3 pt) water, the carrots, celery, onions and parsley. Bring to a gentle boil and simmer for 12 minutes or until fish is done. Boil potatoes in salted water. In a mortar, pound garlic with the bread, season with salt and pepper and gradually add oil, as if you were making mayonnaise. Drain trout, put onto a dish and surround with lemon wedges. Drain potatoes, drizzle with melted butter, and serve with fish; pass aïoli separately.

CHICKEN STUFFED WITH ARTICHOKES

Pollo Ripieno ai Carciofi

SERVES 4

Preheat oven to 180°C/350°F/ gas 4. Crush garlic and rosemary. Put in a bowl with butter, salt and pepper; mix with a wooden spoon until finely creamed. Wash chicken, pat dry and stuff with artichokes and lemon. Sew up opening with cooking thread. Skewer chicken together with a thin skewer, putting 1 sage leaf under each wing and each leg. Rub butter mixture all over chicken, then sprinkle with salt and pepper. Put in a baking pan or dish and pour oil over. Roast for 1½ hours, turning frequently. Remove from oven when golden brown. Transfer to a serving plate and cut into pieces. Arrange artichoke hearts around chicken. Discard lemon. Pour wine into pan and heat over low heat, stirring to blend wine and dripping. Pour sauce over chicken and serve at once.

INGREDIENTS

1 clove garlic

Rosemary sprig

2 tbsp butter

Salt and pepper

1 1¾ kg (about 3 lb) broiler-fryer

4 cooked artichoke hearts

1 lemon, pierced in several places

4 fresh sage leaves

2 tbsp olive oil

About 225 ml (7 floz) dry white wine

21

FRIED STUFFED SARDINES
Sarde Fritte alla Ligure
SERVES 4

Clean sardines, removing heads and tails. Open them out, remove bones, wash and pat dry. Heat a little olive oil in a frying pan, chop mushrooms finely and fry gently for a few minutes. Transfer them to a dish and add fresh bread crumbs, Parmesan, garlic, oregano, 2 eggs and a pinch of salt. Stuff sardines with this mixture, then close them up. Beat remaining 2 eggs with salt and pepper. Dip stuffed sardines first into flour, then into seasoned beaten egg, then into dry bread crumbs. Fry in hot oil and serve immediately.

INGREDIENTS

16 fresh sardines

Olive oil

2 tbsp dried mushrooms, soaked, drained

1 tbsp fresh bread crumbs, softened in a little milk and squeezed dry

1 tbsp grated Parmesan cheese

1 clove garlic, crushed

1 tsp chopped fresh oregano

Pinch of dried leaf oregano

4 eggs

Salt and pepper

plain flour

Fine dry bread crumbs

RED MULLET WITH HAM
Triglie al Prosciutto

SERVES 4

Clean and scale fish; wash, pat dry and season with salt. Wrap each one in a slice of prosciutto. Peel tomatoes, then seed and slice. Cook garlic for 5 minutes in a pan with some oil. Add mullet and cook for 2–3 minutes on each side, turning them gently. Add tomatoes, sprinkle with bread crumbs, season with salt and pepper and cook over low heat for 10 minutes. Sprinkle with parsley and lemon juice. Put mullet on a dish and serve.

INGREDIENTS

12 small red mullet
Salt
12 slices proscuitto
4 ripe tomatoes
1 clove garlic
Olive oil
25 g (1oz) bread crumbs
Pepper
1 tbsp chopped parsley
Juice of ½ lemon

QUAIL IN BRANDY WITH PEAS
Quaglie al Brandy alla Romana

SERVES 4

Wash quail, pat dry and truss each with a skewer. Melt 25 g (1oz) butter in a pan, put in quail and cook briskly for 15 minutes. Moisten with brandy and let this evaporate almost completely. Transfer quail to a serving dish with cooking juices, remove skewers and keep hot. In a separate pan, fry onion in remaining 25 g (1oz) butter, add peas and a little stock, season with salt and pepper, and cook until tender. Just before removing peas from heat, add prosciutto. Garnish the quail with peas and prosciutto and serve.

INGREDIENTS

8 100-175 g (4-6 oz) quail
50 g (2 oz) butter
About 150 g (5 floz) brandy
½ onion, chopped
65 g (2½ oz) shelled fresh peas
Chicken stock
Salt and freshly ground pepper
225 g (½ lb) prosciutto, cut into strips

27

SARDINES WITH PEPPER AND TOMATO SAUCE

Sardine Sotto'olio alla Veneta

SERVES 4

Bone sardines carefully and reassemble them on a serving dish. Decorate with the bell pepper and egg whites. Press tomatoes through a strainer and cream with the butter, sage and garlic. Season with salt and pepper and spoon over the sardines.

INGREDIENTS

12 sardines in oil
1 green or red bell pepper, roasted; skinned, cut into strips
Whites of 3 hard-boiled eggs, chopped
65 g (2½ oz) peeled, seeded, chopped tomatoes
2 tbsp butter
Few fresh sage leaves, chopped
1 clove garlic, crushed
Salt and pepper

RED MULLET LIVORNO STYLE

Triglie alla Livornese

SERVES 4

Wash tomatoes, peel and press through a strainer. In a small pan, heat the butter, 2 tablespoons oil and the basil, then add the tomatoes, season with salt and pepper and cook gently for 30 minutes. Meanwhile, clean and scale fish and remove the fins; wash fish and pat dry. Finely chop celery and garlic. Place celery, garlic, parsley and about 75 ml (2½ floz) oil into pan which you can bring to the table. Fry for a few minutes. Lightly flour the fish and brown on one side. Remove from the heat and very carefully (mullet are fragile) turn them over. Put them back on the heat. Pour over the tomato sauce and cook for about 10 minutes. Serve fish in the pan.

INGREDIENTS

450 g (1 lb) ripe tomatoes

2 tbsp butter

Olive oil

Few fresh basil leaves, chopped

Salt and pepper

4 red mullet or 225 g (½ lb) redfish

1 stalk celery

1 clove garlic

25 g (1 oz) chopped parsley

Plain flour

Chapter Three

Meat Dishes

Veal Kidneys with Mushrooms

■

Genoese Meatballs

■

Potroast Beef with Cinnamon

■

Veal scallops with Ham

■

Tuscan Veal with Ham

■

Steak with Gorgonzola Butter

■

Lamb and Artichoke Casserole

■

Ham Slices with anchovy sauce

■

Pork Chops with Olives

VEAL KIDNEYS WITH MUSHROOMS

Rognone di Vitello al Tegame con Funghi

SERVES 4

Fry onion and garlic in oil, add mushrooms, season with salt and pepper and cook through over medium heat. In another frying pan, sauté kidneys in half the butter and a few tablespoons oil until done. Season, add mushroom mixture and cook briefly. Put on a serving dish, sprinkle with parsley and garnish with bread cut into triangles and fried in remaining butter and a little oil.

INGREDIENTS

1 tbsp chopped onion
1 clove garlic, crushed
Vegetable oil
4 fresh mushrooms, sliced
Salt and pepper
225 g (½ lb) veal kidneys, fat and skin removed
12 g (½ oz) butter
Chopped parsley
2 slices bread

GENOESE MEATBALLS
Polpette alla Genovese
SERVES 4

INGREDIENTS

150 g (3 oz) ground cooked veal

3 tbsp fresh bread crumbs, soaked in stock
or milk and squeezed dry

1 clove garlic, crushed

1 bunch parsley, chopped

Few fresh oregano leaves

2 tbsp dried mushrooms, soaked, drained,
chopped

2 tbsp grated Parmesan cheese

Salt and pepper

Ground nutmeg

1 egg, beaten

Plain flour

Vegetable oil

Solid vegetable shortening

In a bowl, mix the veal, bread crumbs, garlic, parsley, oregano, mushrooms and cheese. Season with salt, pepper and nutmeg; blend in egg, mixing well. Form mixture into balls, flatten slightly and dip in flour. Brown quickly in plenty of oil and shortening, then reduce heat and continue to fry until cooked through. Serve hot.

POT-ROAST BEEF WITH CINNAMON
Arrosto di Manzo alla Cannella

SERVES 4

INGREDIENTS

3 onions, thickly sliced

6 tbsp butter

2 tbsp vegetable oil

800 g (1¾ lb) boneless beef chuck roast

Salt and pepper

Pinch of ground cinnamon

Juice of 1 lemon

300 ml (10 floz) dry white wine

1 bay leaf

Put onions into a pan with butter and oil. Cook over low heat for 5 minutes. Add meat; sprinkle with salt, pepper and cinnamon. Pour in lemon juice and wine, add bay leaf, cover and cook over low heat for 2½ hours, turning meat every so often. When meat is tender, remove from pan, slice and arrange on a serving dish. Pour over the hot sauce from the pan and serve.

VEAL SCALLOPS WITH HAM
Saltimbocca alla Romana
SERVES 4

Flatten veal cutlets and sprinkle with salt and pepper. Cover each cutlet with a slice of prosciutto and a sage leaf, then fold each one in half and secure with a skewer. Flour lightly. Heat 4 tablespoons butter in a frying pan and fry saltimbocca over medium-high heat until brown all over and cooked through. Remove with a slotted spoon and arrange on a serving dish. Add wine to cooking juices and reduce almost completely. Add remaining 1 tablespoon butter and stir until melted; pour hot sauce over saltimbocca. Serve at once.

INGREDIENTS

8 veal cutlets (saltimbocca)
Salt and pepper
8 slices of prosciutto
8 fresh sage leaves
Plain flour
5 tbsp butter
150 ml (5 floz) dry white wine

TUSCAN VEAL WITH HAM
Vitello con Prosciutto alla Toscana
SERVES 4

Season meat with salt and pepper and flour lightly. Melt butter in a heavy saucepan, add a little oil and brown meat. Stir in onion and prosciutto, pour in wine and cook over high heat until liquid is almost evaporated. Cover meat with water and continue to cook, turning meat occasionally. Just before veal is done, add potatoes and stir in garlic, lemon peel and nutmeg; let flavours mingle. Put meat on a serving dish, pour over cooking juices, surround with potatoes and serve.

INGREDIENTS

1 900 g (2 lb) veal rump roast
Salt and pepper
Plain flour
3 tbsp butter
Vegetable oil
1 onion, chopped
100 g (¼ lb) prosciutto, cut into strips
300 ml (10 floz) dry red wine
2 medium potatoes, boiled, peeled, cut into chunks
1 clove garlic, minced
Grated peel of 1 lemon
Ground nutmeg

STEAK WITH GORGONZOLA BUTTER
Bistecche di Manzo con Burrodi Gorgonzola
SERVES 4

INGREDIENTS

6 tbsp butter

25 g (1 oz) crumbled mild gorgonzola cheese

1 tbsp chopped parsley

Lemon juice

4 100 g (4 oz) tender steaks

Salt and pepper

Put 4 tablespoons butter, the gorgonzola, parsley and a few drops of lemon juice into a bowl and beat with a wooden spoon until mixture is smooth and creamy. Roll mixture into a cylinder and wrap in foil. Refrigerate for 1 hour. Melt remaining 2 tablespoons butter in a pan, add steaks and cook over high heat for 2 minutes on each side. Drain, season with salt and pepper and put on a serving dish. Cut gorgonzola butter into 12 slices and put 3 slices on each steak. Serve at once.

LAMB AND ARTICHOKE CASSEROLE
Ragu di Agnello ai Carciofi
SERVES 4

INGREDIENTS

675 g (1½ lb) lean boneless lamb (leg or shoulder), cubed

50 g (2 oz) butter

Vegetable oil

Salt and pepper

Chicken stock

8 cooked artichoke hearts

150 ml (5 floz) dry white wine

Chopped parsley

Brown meat in 5 tablespoons butter and a little oil, season with salt and pepper and cook over low heat until tender, adding stock as necessary. Cut artichoke hearts into strips and cook in remaining 3 tablespoons butter with a pinch of salt. Put lamb onto a dish, add wine to cooking juices and reduce. Pour onto lamb, garnish with artichokes, sprinkle with parsley and serve.

HAM SLICES WITH ANCHOVY SAUCE

Prosciutto Fresco di Maiale Salsato

SERVES 4

INGREDIENTS

8 75 g (3 oz) slices ham

Pepper

Plain flour

2 eggs, beaten

Few tablespoons fresh bread crumbs

7 tbsp butter

1 small onion, chopped

5 flat anchovy fillets, rinsed well, mashed

1 tbsp capers, chopped

1 tbsp chopped parsley

Vinegar

Chicken stock

Flatten ham slices with a mallet and season with pepper; then dip in flour, egg and bread crumbs. Melt 2 tablespoons butter in a pan, add onion and cook over low heat until soft. Add anchovy fillets, capers, parsley, 1 tablespoon flour and a little pepper. Stir over a high heat for a few minutes; stir in 2–3 tablespoons vinegar and let evaporate. Add enough stock to give a slightly thickened sauce. Dice 1 tablespoon butter and stir into sauce a piece at a time, making sure that each piece is fully incorporated before adding the next. Keep warm. In a separate pan, melt remaining 4 tablespoons butter; add breaded ham slices and brown on both sides, then reduce heat and cook for 10–12 minutes, turning occasionally. Arrange on a serving dish, pour over sauce and serve accompanied with buttered spinach.

PORK CHOPS WITH OLIVES
Costolette di Maiale alle Olive
SERVES 4

Peel 18 cloves of garlic; cook for 3 minutes in boiling water, then drain. Flatten chops and insert remaining garlic, cut into slivers. Prepare a marinade with oil, a little vinegar, rosemary, sage, salt and pepper. Put chops in marinade and let stand for 2 hours, turning occasionally. Drain and pat dry. Boil olives in water and cover for 10 minutes, remove from heat and keep hot in cooking liquid. Heat shortening in a pan with 1 tablespoon oil and add chops; brown for 3 minutes on each side. Reduce heat, add drained garlic and continue to cook for 12 minutes longer or until chops are cooked through, turning occasionally. Put chops on a plate and pile garlic and drained olives in the centre. Pour marsala or wine into pan juices and reduce slightly; simmer for 5 minutes, then pour sauce onto the chops. Sprinkle with chopped parsley and serve.

INGREDIENTS

20 cloves garlic

4 pork chops

Vegetable oil

Vinegar

Rosemary sprigs

Few fresh sage leaves

Salt and pepper

40 g (1½ oz) large green olives

1 tbsp solid vegetable shortening

75 ml (2½ floz) marsala or white wine

75 ml (2½ floz) condensed beef bouillon

1 tbsp chopped parsley

47

Chapter Four

Pasta and Primi Piatti

Ravioli with Sage and Pumpkin

■

Sorrel and Egg Pie

■

Spinach Tortelloni Bake

■

Rice with Ham and Chicken Livers

■

Homemade Pasta/Ravioli
Tortellini and Tortelloni

■

Spinach Roman Style

■

Country-Style Peppers and Tomatoes

■

New Onions Escoffies

RAVIOLI WITH SAGE AND PUMPKIN

Ravioli alla Salvia con la Zucca

SERVES 4

Preheat oven to 200°C/400°F/gas 6 . For the pasta, follow instructions on pp.58–59, mixing a pinch of salt with the flour. For the filling, bake pumpkin until tender and scrape flesh into a bowl. Mash pumpkin well. Stir in parmesan, amaretti cookies, and the mustard. Season with salt, pepper and a pinch of nutmeg and mix well. To prepare ravioli, place filling at 5–6½ cm intervals. Boil ravioli in plenty of salted water until al dente. Drain and arrange in layers in a baking dish, topping each layer with melted, browned butter, sage and parmesan. Finish with a sprinkling of parmesan. Bake in oven until golden brown.

INGREDIENTS

For the pasta
450 g (1 lb) plain flour
Salt
5 eggs
1 tsp vegetable oil

For the filling
2 kg (4¼ lb) pumpkin, seeded
50 g (2 oz) grated parmesan cheese
4 crushed amaretti biscuits
Coarse-grained mustard, or Italian fruity mustard, if available
Salt and pepper
Pinch of ground nutmeg

For the sauce
75 ml (2½ floz) melted, browned butter
Few fresh sage leaves, chopped
35 g (1½ oz) grated parmesan cheese

INGREDIENTS

600 g (24 oz) plain flour

Vegetable oil

Salt

900 g (2 lb) sorrel

50 g (2 oz) grated parmesan cheese

Dried Leaf oregano

9 eggs

Pepper

175g (7 oz) ricotta cheese

SORREL AND EGG PIE
Torta Pasqualina
SERVES 4

Pour flour onto a board and make a well in the centre. Mix in 2 tablespoons oil, a pinch of salt and enough lukewarm water to give a dough of same consistency as for homemade pasta (see p. 58-59). Knead for 10 minutes. Divide into 14 pieces and shape each one into a ball. Dust with flour, cover and let stand for an hour. Preheat oven to 200°C/400°F/gas 6. Wash sorrel, discarding any discoloured leaves and large stalks. Put it in a pan with only the water clinging to it, cover and cook gently over low heat, stirring occasionally to make sure it does not stick to pan. When sorrel is cooked (about 8 minutes), squeeze out water, then chop sorrel and place in a bowl. Add 25 g (1 oz) cup parmesan, a pinch of oregano, 3 eggs and the ricotta. Season mixture with salt and pepper, then mix well. Roll out one of the pastry balls very thinly and lay on a greased baking sheet. Sprinkle it with a few drops of oil. Roll out a second pastry ball and lay it on top of the first. Continue rolling, oiling and stacking the pastry balls until you have 7 layers. Put sorrel filling on top. Make 6 dents with back of a spoon and into each break an egg. Season and sprinkle with remaining 25 g (1 oz) parmesan. Roll out other 7 balls until very thin and lay them on top, greasing each one with oil. Prick top sheet with a fork, brush with a little oil and bake in oven for an hour. Allow to cool and serve cold.

SPINACH TORTELLONI BAKE
Tortelloni con Pasta Verde al Gratin
SERVES 4

For the pasta, follow instructions on pages. 58–59. For the filling, thoroughly mix all filling ingredients together. Cut out the pasta, fill and shape into tortelloni (see illustrations 1 and 2 on page 58). For the sauce, cook onion in oil until softened, stir in tomatoes and basil leaves and season with salt and pepper. Cook the tortelloni in boiling salted water until al dente. Layer the tortelloni in a buttered baking dish; dot each layer with butter, sprinkle with parmesan and spread with tomato sauce. Finish with a layer of mozzarella cheese and put into a hot oven until the cheese melts. Serve hot.

INGREDIENTS

For the pasta
230 g (9½ oz) cups all-purpose flour
225 g (½ lb) fresh spinach, cooked, puréd, thoroughly drained
4 eggs

For the filling
150 g (6 oz) ricotta cheese
450 g (1 lb) fresh spinach, cooked, puréed, thoroughly drained
50 g (2 oz) chopped prosciutto
3 tbsp grated parmesan cheese
1 egg yolk
Pinch of ground nutmeg
Salt and pepper

For the sauce
1 small onion, chopped
2 tbsp olive oil
75 g (3 oz) sieved tomatoes
Chopped fresh basil leaves
Salt and pepper
25 g (1 oz) butter
3 tbsp grated parmesan cheese
Sliced mozzarella cheese

RICE WITH HAM AND CHICKEN LIVERS
Risotto alla Trasteverina
SERVES 4

Fry onion in 2½ tablespoons butter, add pancetta, season with salt and pepper and cook gently for 2 minutes. Add marsala or red wine and let it evaporate almost completely. Stir in livers and prosciutto. Add rice and ladle on stock gradually as rice absorbs it, stirring constantly. Remove risotto from heat, stir in remaining 2½ tablespoons butter and a little parmesan. Leave to stand for 1 minute, then serve sprinkled with remaining 2½ tablespoons parmesan.

INGREDIENTS

½ small onion, finely chopped

5 tbsp butter, diced

50 g (2 oz) diced lean pancetta bacon

Salt and pepper

150 g (5 floz) dry marsala *or* red wine

50 g (2 oz) sliced chicken livers

50 g (2 oz) julienne-cut prosciutto

350 g (14 oz) cups rice

Chicken or beef stock

5 tbsp grated parmesan cheese

TORTELLINI AND TORTELLONI

Prepare as right and roll out. Cover pasta with a cloth to avoid drying out, except in area where you are working. There are two basic tortellini shapes: square – like ravioli – and curved triangles with joined edges. When these are large and served as a first course in sauce instead of in a broth, they are often called tortelloni. Below is a simple version of tortelloni verde al gratin.

Place a nut-sized piece of filling – either meat or ricotta and spinach – towards one corner of a square of pasta

Fold the top over to form a triangle and join the points together to make a curved shape

HOMEMADE PASTA
Pasta Fatta in Casa

serves 4

Dust work surface with flour. Mound flour onto board and make a well in the centre. Break eggs into it. Add 1 tablespoon cold water to eggs and 1 or 2 teaspoons oil. Beat eggs with fork and gradually work in flour, using your hands when the dough becomes stiff. Knead for at least 10 minutes. Dough should be stiff – add extra flour if it is too soft. When little air bubbles start to appear, roll dough into a ball, flatten then roll out with a rolling pin as far as possible, making sure that the thickness is uniform,

INGREDIENTS

5 tbsp butter, diced

450 g (1 lb) plain flour

4 medium eggs

vegetable oil

RAVIOLI

Make pasta dough as above, roll pasta into a sheet, dot with filling, and topping with a second sheet cut and into squares.

INGREDIENTS

450 g (2 lb) fresh spinach

Vegetable oil

1 clove garlic, crushed

25 g (1 oz) finely diced bacon

32 tbsp pine nuts

3 tbsp golden raisins, soaked in lukewarm
water until plump

Salt

Butter

SPINACH ROMAN STYLE
Spinaci alla Romana

SERVES 4

Wash spinach, discarding tough stalks and discoloured leaves. Cook gently in water clinging to leaves, then drain and squeeze dry. Heat a little oil in a pan, add garlic, bacon and spinach, and cook, gently stirring. After a few minutes, add pine nuts and golden raisins. Remove from heat, season with salt, put in a serving dish, top with about 1 tablespoon butter and serve.

COUNTRY-STYLE PEPPERS AND TOMATOES
Rusticana alla Piacentina

SERVES 4

Heat butter with some oil in a pan and fry the green onions and peppers until half cooked. If desired you may roast and peel peppers before sautéing with onions. Then add tomatoes, season with salt, add a little lukewarm water and cook over medium heat, stirring occasionally. As soon as peppers are cooked, stir in eggs and serve.

INGREDIENTS

25 g (1 oz) butter

Vegetable oil

450 g (1 lb) green onions

4 large greens or yellow bell peppers, seeded, cut into strips

450 g (1 lb) tomatoes, peeled, seeded, chopped

Salt

4 hard-boiled eggs, chopped

NEW ONIONS ESCOFFIER
Cipolline Novelle alla Escoffier
SERVES 4

INGREDIENTS

800 g (1¾ lb) small white onions

Vegetable oil

Salt and pepper

1 bay leaf

Pinch of dried leaf thyme

1 tsp fennel seeds

3 tbsp golden raisins, soaked in lukewarm water until plump

150 ml (5 floz) dry white wine

About 75 ml (2½ floz) Cognac

Peel onions and boil for 5 minutes. Drain and pat dry. Heat some oil in a pan, add onions, season with salt and pepper and fry gently until golden brown, being careful not to let them burn. Add bay leaf, thyme, fennel seeds and golden raisins, and pour in wine and cognac. Bring to a boil, cover and cook for 5 minutes longer. Remove from the heat, allow to cool and serve.